THE RABBIT HOUSE

The Rabbit House

Laura Alcoba

*Translated from the French
by Polly McLean*

BOOKS

Published by Portobello Books Ltd 2008

Portobello Books Ltd
Twelve Addison Avenue
Holland Park
London W11 4QR

Copyright © Laura Alcoba 2007
This English translation copyright © Polly McLean 2008

First published in France as *Manèges* by Gallimard in 2007

The right of Laura Alcoba to be identified as
the author of this work and Polly McLean's right to
be identified as its translator have been asserted by them
in accordance with the Copyright, Designs and
Patents Act 1988

This book is supported by the French Ministry of
Foreign Affairs as part of the Burgess programme run by the
Cultural Department of the French Embassy in London.
www.frenchbooknews.com

Liberté • Égalité • Fraternité
RÉPUBLIQUE FRANÇAISE

A CIP catalogue record is available
from the British Library

2 4 6 8 9 7 5 3 1

ISBN 978 1 84627 132 8

www.portobellobooks.com

Designed and typeset in Bembo
by Patty Rennie

Printed and bound in the UK by
CPI Mackays Chatham ME5 8TD

For Diana E. Teruggi

A memory, my friend.
We live only in the future or the past.
Gérard de Nerval, *Selected Writings*

YOU MUST BE WONDERING, DIANA, WHY THIS story has taken me so long to write. I promised myself I would do it one day, but kept telling myself that the time hadn't yet come.

In the end I decided it would be better to wait until I was old – very old, even. That seems strange to me now, but for a long time I was quite sure.

It felt important to be more or less alone.

It felt important for the story's few surviving characters to have passed away – or be about to – so I could describe my Argentine childhood without fearing their judgement, or the lack of understanding I felt bound to encounter. I dreaded them asking, 'What's the point of stirring all that up again?' I was uncomfortable, even then, with the idea of having to explain myself. I really thought I would just have to wait for the solitude and freedom of old age.

Then, one day, I couldn't bear to wait any longer. All of a sudden I didn't want to wait to be so old, or so alone. As if I no longer had the time.

This change took place, I'm almost sure, during the trip I took to Argentina with my daughter at the end of 2003. I did some research, and met some people. I started remembering the past in much more detail. In the end, time did its work a great deal faster than I had anticipated: telling the story had suddenly become urgent.

So here it is.

I am going to recall that particular Argentine insanity, and all the people destroyed by its violence. I finally took this step not only because I think about the dead all the time, but also because I know that the survivors must not be forgotten. I have become convinced of how important it is to remember them. To force myself to give them space, too. That's what took me so long to understand, Diana. That's probably the real reason I waited all this time.

But before starting this little story, I would like to tell you one more thing: the fact that I am now gathering together my memories in order to describe the Argentina of the dictatorship, the Montoneros and the reign of terror, all from a child's perspective, is not so much to help me remember as to find out whether, afterwards, I can begin to forget.

I

La Plata, Argentina, 1975

IT ALL STARTED WHEN MY MOTHER SAID TO ME:
'So you see, we'll have a house with a red tile roof and a
garden, too. Just like you wanted...'

*

We have been in our new house for a few days now. It is
far from the city centre, at the edge of the massive waste-
lands surrounding La Plata, where the city has almost
petered out and the pampas hasn't yet begun. In front of
the house there's an old disused railway, and some junk
that seems to have been dumped there a long time ago.
Occasionally, a cow.

Until now we have lived in a small apartment in a concrete and glass tower block on the Plaza Moreno, just next

to my maternal grandparents' house, opposite the cathedral.

I had often fantasized aloud about the house I would like to have lived in, a house with a red tile roof, a garden, a swing and a dog. The kind of house they always have in children's story books. The kind of house I am always drawing, with a big, bright yellow sun just above, and a tub of flowers by the front door.

I feel as if she hasn't understood. When I talked about a house with a red tile roof, it was a manner of speaking. The tiles could have been red or green. What I wanted was the life that went with it. Parents who came home from work every evening for dinner. Parents who baked cakes on Sundays, following recipes from big fat cookery books full of shiny illustrations. A pretty mummy with long, varnished nails and high heels. Or brown boots and a matching handbag. Or no boots, but a big blue coat with a round collar. Or a grey coat. You see, it wasn't really the colour – no more so for the tiles than for the boots or the coat. I wonder how we managed to misunderstand each other so badly. Or perhaps she was just pretending to think that my dreams were simply a matter of gardens, and red.

In any case, the dog was the most important thing.

Or the cat. I can't remember now.

*

She eventually decides to explain some of what's going on. We have left our apartment because, from now on, the Montoneros have to be in hiding. This is necessary because there are some people who have become very dangerous: the men from the AAA squad, the Argentine Anti-communist Alliance, who kidnap militants such as my parents and kill them or make them disappear. So we have to keep ourselves safe, to hide and also to retaliate. My mother explains to me that this is called 'going underground'. 'Now, we are going to go underground' – those were her exact words.

I listen in silence. I understand what my mother is telling me, but I can think of only one question: school. If we are to live in hiding, how will I go to school?

'For you, things will stay the same. Except that you mustn't tell anyone where we live – not even family. We will drop you at the bus stop every morning. You will get off at Plaza Moreno, all by yourself, you'll recognize it, it's easy, the bus stops right in front of Granny and Grandpa's house. They will look after you during the day. We'll find some way to collect you in the evenings.'

*

I'm all alone in a shiny bus, completely covered in red and silver decorations but still ramshackle and dented. The driver's fat hands grip a steering wheel upholstered in green and orange fabric. To the left of the driver there is, today as almost every day, a photo of Carlitos Gardel, wearing his habitual white scarf and with his hat tipped slightly down over his eyes. There's also a picture of the Virgin of Lujan, a tiny lady draped in an enormous sky-blue cloak embellished with golden swirls, crushed by a heavily jewelled crown as well as all the rays emanating from her glorious body. Then there are stickers informing passengers that the driver is a supporter of the Gimnasia y Esgrima de La Plata football team. To make things really clear, he has stuck a little blue and white flag with a faded fringe to the back of his seat. As for the big sticker strip across the upper part of the windscreen, in the Argentine colours, all the drivers have that whether they're supporters of Estudiantes or even Boca Juniors, the great Buenos Aires team.

The roads in our new neighbourhood are riddled with deep potholes, through which the buses and cars attempt to navigate the gentlest way possible. Luckily, the bumps start to decrease as we approach town, and the Plaza Moreno.

*

I won't mention the hatch in the ceiling. I promise. Not to the men who might come and ask questions, not even to my grandparents.

Mummy and Daddy hide newspapers and weapons in there, but I mustn't say a word. The others don't know that we have been forced to go to war. They wouldn't understand. Not yet, anyway.

Mummy has told me about a little boy who saw the hiding place his parents had created behind a painting – but the parents had forgotten to tell the child how important it was to keep quiet. He was very young; he could barely talk. They must have thought there was no point, he wouldn't be able to say anything to anyone, and wouldn't understand their warnings in any case.

When the police arrived at their house, they rummaged through the whole place without finding a thing. Not a single weapon, no militant newspapers, not even a banned book. Which is saying something, considering how many books were on the list of banned publications. But nothing in these people's house could have been considered 'subversive'. The thing is, these rummaging men hadn't thought to look behind the painting.

They were getting ready to leave, they were almost out of the door, when one of them turned around and retraced his steps. It had suddenly occurred to him that during their search the little boy, that same little boy who could barely say a few words, had several times pointed to a painting, saying '*Ahí! Ahí!*' The man took down the painting... and now the whole family is in prison, all because of a little boy who barely knew how to speak.

But with me, things are very different. I am big. I may be only seven years old, but everyone says that I already talk and think like a grown-up. It makes them laugh that I know the name of Firmenich, the head of the Montoneros, and even the words of the Peronist Youth chant off by heart. They have explained everything to me. I have understood and I will obey. I won't say a word. Even if someone were to hurt me. Even if they twisted my arm or burnt me with an iron. Even if they drove little nails into my knees. You see, I have understood how important it is to keep quiet.

*

I have finally arrived at my grandparents' place. Once again, I am welcomed by the voice of Julio Sosa. My grandfather is listening to tango, as he does every morning before leaving for his office in Buenos Aires.

He is a lawyer, but he never takes political cases. He

doesn't want any trouble. He has always defended small-time drug dealers, forgers, tax evaders, con artists of all kinds. My grandfather is very fond of these little thugs, who in return often display a kind of brotherly gratitude to him. Although, once, one of them who had been temporarily taken in by my grandparents did go off with the bathtub. No one in the house blamed him for having been tempted, though. It was a beautiful tub, marble, a real collector's item. Proof that he knew his trade.

In any case, there is nothing to fear with these guys (apart from the inconvenience of replacing the beautiful bathtub, and the occasional disappearance of some valuable object). My grandfather has always thought that these young hoodlums are 'good people'. Apart from a few rather comic misadventures − told ironically, constantly embellished with new contexts and details, towards the end of almost every Sunday lunch, when my mother's many sisters love to spar with each other: who can recount with the greatest wit the funny stunts one or other of these punks has dared pull in the very house their protector had been kind enough to welcome them into? − nobody ever has any reason to complain. Quite the opposite. When they don't leave with a bathtub under their arm, they are always happy to help in any way they can − these are the handymen, the patchers-up of daily life. But they aren't remotely involved in politics. They don't want to change the world, just to indulge in a little fiddling of the world-as-it-is. What makes my grandfather nervous are the people who want everything to change.

*

I am about to leave for school, with my uncle (my mother's little brother), my grandmother and my aunt Sofia.

Sofia isn't right in the head, but you mustn't mention it. She's like a child. She barely knows how to write.

She helps out in the office at my school. She fetches the registers from the classes, and serves maté to the teachers during break. She thinks it's a job, but in actual fact my grandfather gives the headmistress an envelope every month, which she in turn gives to Sofia, taking good care to conceal from her the origin of what she thinks is her pay cheque. This little white lie makes her feel useful; she really thinks that they need her, to the extent of paying her. My grandparents think it does her good, and in any case what else would they do with her all day?

In the evenings, after dinner, my grandmother always drops me off at her brother Carlitos's place.

This is because of the lady who knits.

For the past few months, there has been a black car parked outside my grandmother's house all day long. Inside, there is always a blonde lady, severely dressed, with a chignon perched high on her head, knitting. She looks a little like Isabel Perón, but much younger and more beautiful. She sometimes has a man with her, but most of the time she's alone. We wait for her to leave before going over to Carlitos's place, where Mummy collects me.

*

Today, at my grandmother's brother's house, I scarcely had time to play with the dog. My parents came to collect me, together this time, and much earlier than usual. We drove off towards our house with the red tile roof.

There aren't many traffic lights in our new neighbourhood. When you come to a crossroads you have to beep loudly, to warn any cars that are driving along it.

Our conversations in the car become jerky; we try not to lose the thread of our sentences as they are interrupted by the blast of horns. The beeps come from every direction: right, left; sometimes from just a few metres in front or behind, blaring out all over the place. The signals might seem confusing, but actually you just have to get used to it. The person driving always seems to know exactly which warning is meant for him.

Today, my father hooted as usual, but the car coming along the crossroad didn't stop or slow down. The impact was very violent and my head bashed against the windscreen.

The most important thing is not to stop. The police might turn up, to see what's going on. There's that hatch at home... and my parents haven't yet received their false papers because it takes a long time to make false papers that the police might take for real. And also, I forgot to say, our red 2CV is stolen.

The car is spluttering, and no longer seems able to stop. It stalls, my father starts it again, it stalls once more... We abandon our lovely French car on the side of the road and run hastily into the side streets, not even looking over our shoulders.

2

EVERY DAY AFTER SCHOOL, I GO TO MY GRAND-
parents' place for a while, with Sofia and Luis, my mother's
little brother who attends the same school as me.

Sofia is supposed to keep an eye on us on the walk
home. It's another part of her 'job'. But actually, my uncle
and I do exactly as we please. We rush ahead, or else
pretend to retrace our footsteps, as if we had turned back
time and it was now time to go to school, not return from
it. Whatever we do, Sofia freaks out. It's great fun making
her run after us: 'Stop! Wait for me!' She's really comical,
with her ill-fitting adult's body – so much too tall and too
fat for her, who's so clumsy and lost.

When we get to my grandmother's we have a snack.

The same Julio Sosa cassette is always playing. *El Varón del Tango.* The name is on the cover.

*

The knitting lady isn't there today. Perhaps they realized that we had realized? Unless someone else has taken over – the Plaza Moreno, opposite my grandmother's house, is always packed full of people.

A man reading a newspaper on a bench, people taking a stroll, lovers lying on the grass stroking and kissing each other, really taking their time, and as usual masses of children.

Never mind: we are on the alert. My grandmother and I – or sometimes one of my aunts takes me – go over to Carlitos's after nightfall. We always stop several times on the way, to check whether anyone is following us. It's just a matter of habit.

Often, it's me who checks behind. It's more normal for a child to stop and turn around – in an adult it could be seen as suspicious behaviour, proof of nervousness, and might attract attention. But I have learnt to make these checks into a game. I do three little hops, clap my hands and jump right around, both feet at once. Between my grandmother's house and her brother Carlitos's place there is time to do this at least ten times, and in this way I can check, as natural as can be, that no one is tailing us.

If I suspect anything, I tell the adult who's accompanying me. We stop at a shop window or act as if we've lost our way, while we work out what's going on.

Today, things don't follow their usual pattern. My grandmother tells me that my mother has just phoned. We won't be going to Carlitos's place tonight. My father has been arrested. I'll have to stay with my grandparents until my mother gives us more news. She said she would phone back. But when?

*

I eventually went to visit my father in prison, with my paternal grandparents.

We were in a big cobblestone courtyard and it was very sunny.

My father was all dressed in blue, like the others, with his head almost shaved. There were other men of my father's age, whose children and parents had also come to visit for the first time. It seemed as if that prison held only new prisoners. And we were new, too, today – new visitors.

Just before we entered the courtyard, a tall, beautiful

lady dressed in a suit and perched on very high heels searched my grandmother and me, as well as the other women, while my grandfather, in his group of men, had to go with a short, fat policeman, who was very dark and had a thick, bushy moustache.

The search took place in a tiny room, which the visiting women entered one at a time. I went in with my grandmother. At first, I thought to myself that my grandmother and I were lucky to be searched by such an elegant lady – look, she has a chignon, too – but I didn't like it when she squeezed me all over.

My grandmother was left standing in her bra and knickers for a long time. Her breasts were very large, and so flabby and drooping. She seemed uncomfortable with me looking at her. I felt strange as well, to tell the truth, because of those breasts, and also the little purple and blue marks on her thighs, which I had never noticed before.

The beautiful suited lady certainly took her time frisking my grandmother. She slipped a hand between her breasts, lifting them repeatedly, one at a time, and even kneading them like soft, shapeless dough. She also squeezed her buttocks, and put a hand between her thighs.

We made a strange bunch, in the sunny courtyard of La Plata prison. Sitting in rows, in bright sunlight – you might have thought we'd all met up to commemorate something. But it was a strange kind of gathering because those dressed in blue didn't leave at the end.

My father asked me to write to him every week. He said that reading my letters would help him. We didn't mention my mother, or the hatch, or any of that. We tried to talk about this and that. Casually, as if nothing was happening.

Then my grandfather asked my father how he was, and my father asked my grandfather how he was, and then it was my turn to answer the same question. Each of us said that everything was fine.

3

TODAY, MY GRANDFATHER AND I HAVE A DATE with my mother. How long is it since I've seen her? Two months, maybe three?

We go to meet her in one of the pretty La Plata squares, all white flagstones and trees in blossom. Apparently my mother has told us to meet her next to the merry-go-round.

My grandfather suggests a stroll around the square, but I don't want to. I sit next to him on a bench and stare at my shoes, holding his hand as the merry-go-round spins and the party music blares out, all silly bells and shrill noise.

It's a very sunny day, but the sun is bothering me so I screw up my eyes.

What I like about screwing up my eyes in such strong

sunlight is that it lets me see things differently. Most of all I love the moment when the shape of things starts to blur and suddenly flatten.

When the sun shines as intensely as it is today, it's easier to get to that place where everything changes, and all at once I see myself amid images that are all flattened, almost as if they've been stuck onto a sheet of shiny paper. Simply by screwing up my eyes, I manage to push everything around me back, push it far away, flatten it all out against a light-filled background. Even the fairground music ends up crushed against this wall of light.

Once I have reached this place, I do my best to hold on to it for as long as I can. But the strange new perspective always fades away, sometimes as soon as I've reached it. And this time, the very shape of things resists me. In a flash, everything reverts to 3-D and the book of light in which I had found myself disappears.

But I try for the experience again because I'm stubborn, and I love making things flatten out like this with the mere strength of my gaze. So I push everything around me away, crushing it once more into the background. Even my grandfather. This time, it all flattens very quickly, as if I had managed to draw upon my brief previous experience.

But it's as if the merry-go-round, the trees, my grand-father and the bells have become stronger too. Despite the force with which I saw them flatten, here they are becoming 3-D again, even faster and more energetically than before. I give up the fight – for now.

My grandfather stands up. My mother must have arrived.

The world had been back as it should be for too long. The trees, the merry-go-round, the children. Only my mother was missing.

I stand up, too, and see a woman who seems to be the one we are waiting for, judging from Grandfather's behaviour – but I can't recognize her.

My mother no longer looks anything like my mother. This is a skinny young woman with short red hair. Extremely red, a red I have never seen on hair before. I flinch away as she leans down to hug me.

'It's me, Mummy. Don't you recognize me? It must be the hair...'

My grandfather and my mother exchange a few short words.

From what I can gather, she is trying to reassure him.

Then the sun starts shining even more brightly than before. And the red hair stuck on the head of the woman who has come to find me starts to flame. What a racket, this is deafening. Once again, I screw up my eyes, as hard as I can, much harder than before. In vain.

From now on, one thing is for sure – the light is no longer on my side.

My grandfather leaves and we head in the other direction, far from the merry-go-round and the sunny square.

*

As always when I see my mother again after a long separation, she offers to buy me a doll.

When my parents went to prison for the first time (I must have been three or four years old, perhaps a little more), I remember that when they came back they gave me a blonde plastic mermaid holding a little baby in her arms. A tiny baby that the little blonde mermaid seemed to be cradling with great affection.

That time, in order not to upset me, my grandparents had decided to tell me that my mother and father had 'gone to Cordoba for work'. But I knew that they were in prison, and that none of it had anything to do with their work, but rather with a trip to Cuba they had made a long time before. Somehow, in my mind, my parents' first imprisonment and my plastic mermaid became linked to the town of Cordoba and also a little to Havana, even though in fact the prison was much more local, and my little plastic mermaid was probably bought in our own neighbourhood. It doesn't matter – every time I look at her, even though I know perfectly well it's not true, I feel as if my parents travelled a long, long way to find this doll for me – to the tropics or somewhere like that. So, even though I know that Cordoba is actually completely irrelevant, I call her 'my little blonde Cordoba mermaid', and that's why she's my favourite doll. And in any case it's true: the more I look at her, the more sure I am that she's from some exotic place, far away.

This time, I can choose my reunion doll myself. We walk into a shop and my mother says:

'Pick whichever one you like.'

I stop in front of a plump, chubby-cheeked doll with long curly brown hair. My mother pays quickly at the till, murmuring a few barely audible words to the saleswoman; she seems to understand that she needn't wrap it, and we leave immediately.

My mother takes me by the hand.

With my other hand I squeeze the hand of the pretty dolly who is coming with me.

4

I'M NOT SURE WHERE WE ARE ANY MORE, NEVER mind where we're going. The square and its merry-go-round are already a long way behind us. My red-headed mother strides firmly on, not saying a word to me. I trot beside her, holding on to her hand and the dolly, not daring to break the silence.

We arrive in a part of town I don't know, with little low houses and deserted streets. At the corner of one street no different from all the others, we open a door and walk down a long corridor. It opens onto a yard planted with trees, where five or six little modern houses have been built right up against each other. Their identical blue, street-level doors are each accompanied by the same puny little shrub, which seems to have been plonked there against its will and doesn't look likely to last long. It's already night-time.

A woman I have never seen before opens one of the doors, and closes it again as soon as we're inside. She leads us into the house in silence. She was clearly waiting for us, for my mother and me; she hugs us as if she has known us for years, and seems happy that we have arrived. Perhaps I have met her, in the past? Perhaps she has changed her appearance, too, just like my mother, who used to be a long-haired brunette and now has short red hair?

In the house, everything is silent. The white walls are completely plain. The shutters are closed. The whole house seems lit by a single bulb hanging from the kitchen ceiling, and a little desk lamp on the floor of the adjoining room, whose concrete floor awaits a softer covering it will probably never receive. The lady quickly shows us the room. It is plunged in darkness, apart from the little circle of light thrown onto the floor by the metal lamp, a tiny halo in a room made oversized by its complete lack of furniture, apart from a few old fruit crates used as a book-case, and two mattresses on the floor. There are lots of books, books everywhere, as well as magazines and masses of papers, clumsily stacked in unstable columns, which I imagine collapsing at the slightest touch. We return to the kitchen, where my mother and the lady lean against a wall to talk.

The woman starts talking about God. My mother listens very intently. As for me, I think this is one of the first times I have heard God discussed as if he really existed, as if he were a real person, someone you could count on. Of course, I have seen my great-grandmother saying her rosary daily, almost mechanically, barely moving her lips and with her eyes closed. She would slide the beads of her rosary between her fingers, one by one, as she repeated prayers that followed on from each other so continuously that you could make out only the odd word. This activity always seemed to me to belong to family folklore.

The lady convinces my mother that I must be baptized, as a matter of urgency.

I didn't know I hadn't been.

To tell you the truth, I had never thought about it.

I am stunned to hear all this, but most of all reassured to learn that you can count on God, and that you just have to make Him a sign and He will take care of those who have need of Him.

My mother and this woman turn towards me and tell me about the first Christians. They speak to me directly, and then start to talk among themselves again with such enthusiasm that they seem to forget I'm there. The lady says that God isn't only to be found in the churches. In fact, you could be forgiven for wondering if He can still be found there at all – with all that's happening, would He still feel at home there? This notion really cracks them up: the two of them seem to think it's a great joke. I laugh, too, at the idea of an evicted, wandering God, a bit like us now. I look from one to the other trying to laugh very loud, as loud as I can, hoping to remind them of my presence, and show them that I have understood the joke.

At least, I think I have.

Anyway, it seems that God is very approachable – you just have to make Him a sign and to believe in Him. This is called hope, or faith.

The word 'hope' seems to me more straightforward.

This evening, we are going to invoke Him ourselves, without recourse to a priest. A little water, a few prayers, and I, too, can be a Christian.

Just like the times of the first Christians in fact, explains the lady, when God and Christ were with the lowly, who were in hiding, just like us. I think I understand, and I feel very close to the men and women who came before us, so long ago. So God is watching over us, right now, as He watched over them, in the past?

All of a sudden, I, too, feel a sense of urgency.

I want to be placed under the protection of God as soon as possible. I can't understand how I managed to live without Him for so long. Not even knowing what I was missing.

I undress in the kitchen and hop into a large metal tub, like the one my grandmother used for washing delicate fabric. Or dishcloths, when they were really filthy.

My mother's friend prays in a barely audible voice, with her eyes closed, as she pours water over my head. Her prayers are followed by a long silence – she must be waiting for a sign, for His reply. Then she takes my mother's hands and the two of them make a little circle around me, like when you dance in a ring, except that they stay still and quiet.

The wait seems incredibly long, interminable.

He certainly takes His time, replying.

In the little kitchen of the little empty house, we wait.

What if He doesn't respond? What if He doesn't want me? What if I was wrong to laugh at the thought that He was displaced? What if His wanderings have weakened Him for ever, separating Him permanently from us, and from all mankind?

I don't dare move.

Eventually, the lady opens her eyes. As if someone had

given her permission – as if obeying a signal, which may not have reached as far as me but in which I already do not doubt, do not wish to doubt – she makes the sign of the cross on my forehead.

I feel extraordinarily soothed and relieved. So He did reply. He does want me.

I step out of the water and put my clothes back on, feeling quite different already.

5

MY MOTHER AND I VISIT A NEW HOUSE, WHERE WE meet a young couple. Their names are Daniel and Diana, but we soon start calling them Cacho and Didi.

Diana is pregnant, although you can hardly tell. She has long, pale, wavy hair, and extremely bright, large, soft green eyes. She is very beautiful, and very smiley.

I immediately feel that her smile is doing me good. It soothes me in the same way as the baptism in the metal tub. Perhaps even more. But I can also tell that this smile belongs to days gone by, to something I know has been lost for ever. And yet, how reassuring to see that it has managed to survive enough to alight here, on this particular face.

My mother tells me that soon we will live with Cacho and Didi in another house, far from the city centre. The two of them smile at me – I see Diana's face most clearly, because it is so radiant – and ask me what I think of that, whether I like the idea. I say yes, trying to smile myself, but knowing full well that my own smile will be ridiculous next to Diana's, next to that hair and those eyes.

*

While we wait to move into that new house we live with a couple who have two children, boys of about my age.

I play with them a bit, games that are completely new to me. The three of us never talk about what's going on, or about living underground – did someone explain to them, as they did to me? – or about the war that we are immersed in, despite the city being full of people who aren't taking part, and who sometimes don't seem to realize that it's even happening. If they're just pretending not to realize, they're doing a very good job.

We don't talk about the fear, either. They ask no questions – not about what I'm doing here, at their house, alone with my mother; not even how long we are going to stay. It's incredibly reassuring that these questions don't exist, that they are tactful enough to spare me.

So I pick up a little red car and push it along a table, making the noise of a motor at full throttle, or else the rush of wind against the car's bodywork. To tell the truth, I am copying the younger boy, who is doing exactly the same thing as me but lying on the floor, on his back, pushing his car along the underside of the table, as if the driver and his car have managed to escape the laws of gravity. I don't really understand the point of this game, but I want to show willing so I apply myself as best I can.

At the other end of the table, the older boy pushes the wreck of a little green car, which has lost a door and part of whose roof has caved in, along the edge of the table, likewise alternating the sounds of engine, wind and a few keen workings of the brakes; when he gets to the end of his road he goes back to the beginning, just as we do – his brother and I. We play like this for a long time, both separately and together. Sometimes one of us responds to the other's roar with a fierce gust of wind against which each of our machines must do battle.

Suddenly, the little brother makes us jump with a shrill hoot of his horn.

*

Today there's a meeting. Once again, it's taking place in a new house. The man we are staying with will drive my mother and me there.

We get into the back. A very young, handsome man sits in the front, next to the driver. We turn right into one street, and then immediately into another. When we reach a park-like square we drive around it twice, maybe three times, as if re-creating on the tarmac the movements of the merry-go-round, which is spinning fast but in the opposite direction in the middle of the square. I suddenly realize that it's the same square my grandfather took me to a few days before; there's the little toy shop where I chose my reunion dolly. In the shop window I see a doll with exactly the same face and hair as mine, but different clothes. She seems to me a little taller, and more lovely. I shout to my mother:

'Look! They had others, but that one is different. She's got more hair, and it's shinier!'

My mother doesn't reply. We drive past my doll again, the same but different.

'Look! There were others like mine, but this one isn't the same. Her lips are much brighter red, too!'

My mother still doesn't reply. It's the driver who speaks to me, harsh, clearly extremely annoyed:

'Shut up, will you! Just shut up!'

It's the only time he speaks to me.

Hurt by his words and by my mother's persistent

silence, I turn towards her and see that she has her eyes closed. The man says to her:

'I'm sorry, but I'll have to go right back to the beginning. Tell her, won't you, and get her to shut up. Shit!'

And so she explains:

'I'm closing my eyes so that I don't see where we're going, and he is going round and round to make me completely lose track of where I am. Do you understand? It's for safety.'

I understand.

But I can see… If my mother closes her eyes, will that protect me, too? I keep all my questions to myself though, and my mouth shut. In any case, we never passed that doll again – the same as mine but better.

*

We finally move in with Cacho and Didi.

Actually, we join them in a little house they seem to have moved into a few days earlier, meaning that it's their place, even if it will be our place a bit, too.

The little house has rusty green railings, separating the tiny front yard from a pavement, which isn't quite a pavement but an assortment of pebbles, sand, paving stones and mounds of earth that become great muddy pools when it rains, which is very often as it's almost the end of summer. The road hasn't been laid with tarmac, as is often the case on the outskirts of the city. In dry weather our neighbours pour buckets of water on the section of road in front of their door, to prevent the wind from making too much dust. This helps keep the earth on the ground. The best is when it rains, but not too hard, because too much rain makes the road unusable – for cars as well as the many pedestrians and horses that move about this part of La Plata. Then, the whole neighbourhood gets stuck in the mud.

The front door leads onto a corridor. Cacho and Didi live in the room to the right of this. On the left, there's a door through to the garage. These are the only two rooms facing the road. At the end of the corridor is a relatively large kitchen, which we use as a living and dining room, too. At the far end of this multipurpose room, in line with the corridor and the front door, is another door opening onto a courtyard. Looking onto the courtyard from the right is a rather ramshackle, windowless toilet. Facing the kitchen door is another door, which opens onto the tiny room in which my mother and I sleep. It is all very compact, but the house doesn't stop there.

At the far end of the courtyard, behind the room shared

by my mother and me, there is a very basic warehouse, a sort of dilapidated shed, which — contrary to what a visitor who didn't know the group might expect — is actually the very heart of the house. This run-down space, covered over by nothing more than a few sheets of rusty corrugated tin, is what made the Montonero leadership select this particular house for us.

6

THE BUILDING WORKS NEED TO BE DONE FAST. THE *embute* will be built at the far end of the shed, at the far end of the house.

But first, we've got to dig a big hole.

For the past few days, two men – the Labourer and the Engineer – have been coming to work at the house. Diana picks them up in her little grey van. Once it's inside the garage, she opens the back door to let them out of their hiding place and out of the darkness – because they always make the journey from where they meet Diana to our house hidden under a dusty old blanket. When they emerge, their eyes take a while to adjust to the light.

We always spend a moment together in the kitchen, before they start work on our massive hole. Most of the time they talk with Diana and my mother, sometimes with Cacho but not so often as he isn't usually around. During that time, my job is to serve the maté.

The reason Cacho doesn't tend to be there is that he's still lucky enough to have a job – and in his real name, too. Nobody knows that he's a Montonero, and the same goes for Diana, who looks exactly like the pretty blonde wife of a normal business executive.

He usually leaves for Buenos Aires early in the morning, and doesn't come back till late at night. He works in an office, and must have a very important job: in any case, he is always dressed up to the nines. He usually wears a navy blue suit, a tie slightly lighter blue than the suit, and a spotless white shirt. With his black leather briefcase and smart moustache, he looks nothing like a 'revolutionary'.

This get-up amuses Cesar enormously. Cesar is the leader of the group, and comes to the house by bus or on foot. Apart from the people who live here – Cacho, Diana, my mother and me – he's the only member of the organization who knows where the house is, which means he can come over independently, once a week, to chair the meetings.

Cesar is slightly older than the others. He must be thirty years old. His little round glasses make him look rather academic. He also has laughing eyes and straight, dishevelled hair, making him look a bit like a poet, too. And why not – an academic poet.

Cesar always exclaims, laughing: 'You look fantastic, Cacho, that tie, really… although you could allow yourself the odd extravagance… I don't know… a pale grey tie, perhaps…'

Cesar always makes the same jokes, but they always make us laugh anyway.

All this is why Cacho and Diana were selected: partly to put us up, but more importantly to accommodate at their place a particularly sophisticated *embute*, which must be perfectly protected.

Protected by a perfect couple, who are above all suspicion and expecting a child.

A couple like any other that an academic poet might visit on a regular basis.

As for my mother and me… we are simply visiting, for a while. But my mother is a very shy, quiet woman who clearly prefers to keep herself to herself.

*

Since the building works started, about ten days ago, the Labourer has filled dozens of sacks with earth and rubble.

At the end of the day, before it gets dark, the Labourer and the Engineer – or sometimes only one of them, in which case it's always the Labourer, as the Engineer often doesn't need to come – get back under the dusty old blanket so Diana can drive them home. Once it's pitch dark, Diana or Cacho take the van out again, this time to dump the few sacks that have been filled up that day on one of the many nearby areas of wasteland, or at another building site.

Sometimes we leave one on the pavement, where the neighbours can see.

This is because officially we are doing some work on the shed so we can keep rabbits in there. These visible sacks justify – we hope – the endless comings and goings of the grey van. In this way we flaunt the busyness and waste materials appropriate to a modest rabbit breeding project. But behind the rabbit breeding area is concealed a whole other building site, huge, on another scale entirely – because the house we live in was chosen to hide the secret Montonero printing press.

The two building sites are being worked on at the same time, and each day we see a little more progress: while kilos and kilos of earth are dug out to create the small secret room where the printing press will be hidden, the shed is stacked with dozens of metal cages intended to house the rabbits that will soon be joining us.

*

During the daytimes, as I wait for school to (hopefully) start again, I observe the progress of the building site, or rather the two building sites, the official and the other. It was the Engineer who dreamed up the secret room that is being built at the far end of the shed. He has designed a second wall in front of the back wall, perfectly parallel, no more than two metres in front of the original wall, perhaps even less. Now that the building works have progressed this far, and the right-hand side of the second wall has already been built, you can make out a thick door, made from the same material as the wall but framed by a metal structure.

The Engineer is really very talented. He is proud of his work, now almost complete, and explains to me that the *embute* he has devised is one of the most complex ever built.

An electronic mechanism controls the opening and closing of the thick concrete door, giving access to the hidden printing press.

'What do you mean, an electronic mechanism?'

'Yes. You see, these two electric wires will remain exposed, just here, as they often do on building sites, when the work hasn't been completely finished. But in this case, it will not be carelessness… I'm nearly there, now. Watch, we'll try it out.'

And then he does something unbelievable, right in front of my eyes. With the help of two other wires connected to a little box, he establishes a connection that makes the enormous concrete door in front of us move, incredibly fast: the space intended for the clandestine printing press suddenly disappears behind a wall in which you couldn't imagine there being an opening. The metallic structure framing the door has also become invisible: in closing, the door has made it vanish out of sight.

I squeal in admiration; the mechanism is awe-inspiring. The Engineer is visibly pleased with himself, and starts explaining his masterpiece. When the door is shut, it is absolutely flush with the wall and no one could guess it existed. If we need to hide the *embute*'s contents, all we have to do is pick up this box, which we will always leave in the corner, but in full view, as if it had simply been left there.

Now that really is smart – in fact it's what he's most proud of, he says: that this complex, ingenious mechanism is protected by signs of supposed negligence and pseudo carelessness which are in fact absolutely intentional.

'The opening mechanism of the *embute* is all the better hidden because the tools needed to work it are visible to the naked eye. Not bad, eh? I got the idea from an Edgar Allen Poe story: nothing is as well hidden as when it is *excessively obvious*. If I had completely hidden the whole mechanism, it wouldn't have been as well protected. These crude wires I have left exposed are the best possible camouflage. The carelessness, the simple display of it, is absolutely on purpose, and is precisely what protects us. The rabbits will protect us, too, when they arrive...'

'So is Edgar Allen Poe good, then?'

'Masterful, I should say! "The Gold-Bug", "The Fall of the House of Usher", "Ligeia"... you'll read them all when you grow up.'

'Oh, really? Can't I read them now?'

'You could always try now, sure, but I doubt you'd really pick up the nuances...' the Engineer replies, before walking into the *embute* to check the connections inside the secret chamber.

His voice is noticeably muffled:

'My favourite is "The Purloined Letter".'

*

Every time the Engineer arrives for work I rush over to the building site. The Labourer is always here because he also has to build the living arrangements for the soon-to-arrive rabbits. But the Engineer visits less and less often.

'It's all working perfectly now. Soon you won't be seeing me any more.'

Turning towards me as he yet again checks the mechanism to open and close the door of the *embute*, he says these words with a big smile that lights up his whole face.

I have never noticed how handsome he is. His hair is very dark, almost black, but his skin is pale and creamy. As for his eyes, I couldn't say exactly what colour they are. Grey blue, grey green? The thing is, his eyes change colour with the weather and the light, and also, I think, with his own will, with the glow he wishes to give them: sometimes, his gaze becomes closed, veiled with a sort of impenetrable layer that gives it a darker glint. The Engineer must be the same age as my father, but he seems much taller and more slender. I feel so young, next to him...

Leaning against the false back wall of the house, I start playing with a lock of my hair, coiling it around my finger, my head tilted slightly to one side.

'Oh... that's a shame. What you've done is so brilliant,

48

really... perhaps you could design another *embute*, a smaller one, somewhere else in the house. I don't know... in the living room, or my bedroom, for instance.'

He turns back to me and bursts out laughing.

'No! I've finished my work here... I've got other things to do.'

I feel so stupid for asking. I think I even blush, when I hear him burst out laughing. I squeeze my hands really tight behind my back, and rush off to my room, pretending not to care but in fact deeply hurt.

*

Next to my bed is a little chest of drawers where my mother and I keep our things.

I pretend to tidy it up, embarrassed by the scene with the Engineer and hoping to forget what a fool I have made of myself with my proposition. I was trying to behave like an adult, a militant, the lady of the house, but I should have known I am young, so young, so incredibly young, and that if the Engineer seemed to enjoy our conversations, it was only because I was always there, and so as not to upset me.

I keep rummaging around in the drawers, pulling my clothes out and refolding them and putting them back in different places: keeping busy while I wait for this to pass.

I feel something hard, tucked behind a jumper... Oh, it's the old camera my aunt Silvia gave me the last time I saw her. She had just bought herself another, better camera, and so she gave me this one. 'Here,' she said when she held it out to me, 'I'm giving you my old camera. It's not fantastic, but it'll do for your first photos.'

I had completely forgotten it was there.

What photos can I take in this room?

There are two single iron beds and a shelf on which I have put two stuffed frogs – very soft frogs, as they are stuffed with sand. Their backs are completely green, but my grandmother, who made them for me, made sure to cover their bellies in a pretty flowered fabric. That way, she told me, it'll look as if they're taking a siesta on a bed of water lilies.

When I look at them through the lens, I struggle to recognize them: because they are so soft they don't hold their shape, and just look like two greenish lumps on the shelf above my bed. I can't even make out their flowery bellies.

The thing is, through the lens of my camera our little room looks even darker than it actually is. Engulfed by this darkness, one thing is for sure – my frogs don't show up at all.

So I point my camera towards the window that looks out onto the courtyard.

On the other side of the yard, on the wall opposite my bedroom window, the lens distinctly shows up a few damp patches and even a thin but deep crack through the middle of the wall. I take a few steps closer to the window because it's obvious that my camera picks up what's happening outside much more clearly.

It's then that I hear the footsteps of the Engineer moving from the back of the house towards the kitchen. In a moment, he will pass in front of the window to my bedroom.

I am glad to have the camera: it will allow me to look at him without staring like an idiot. I feel a bit protected, behind the camera. I would like him to look at me, too, and see me differently at last, with my grown-up instrument.

I can already see him through the lens, but he doesn't appear to have noticed me.

Just as the Engineer is about to step out of the courtyard and be swallowed into the kitchen, I make a little noise, a 'click' to attract his attention, flashing him a big smile from behind the black box obscuring my face.

Instead of going into the kitchen he bursts furiously

into my room, and snatches the camera from my hands.

'You must be insane! What the hell are you doing?!'

He opens the case angrily and sees that it is empty. He throws it down on the bed and grabs my arm, which he grips tightly and shakes hard.

'This is not funny, not funny at all! You know we can't take photos, for God's sake! This isn't some kind of holiday camp!'

'But there's no film; it was just a game.'

He recovers himself a little, but adds, still upset and panting:

'Just don't play that game any more, OK!'

I look down and start crying. Very quietly. I don't want him to see my tears, but soon I can't suppress a sob, stifled but still perfectly noticeable. The more I try to hold back my tears the more intensely my body is shaken by sobs, and by the effort itself.

He wheels around sharply, as if to leave, but then gets hold of himself. He forces himself to speak to me in a much gentler voice. But his voice is softened too suddenly and artificially to be able to soothe me:

'I'm sorry. We're all very keyed up, you do understand that, don't you?'

And he taps lightly on the top of my head with the

tips of his fingers, while I remain still, head down, plaits hanging.

This timid tapping by way of apology simply completes the humiliation.

7

WHEN I THINK OF THE MONTHS WE SHARED WITH Cacho and Didi, the first thing that comes to mind is that word *embute*. And yet, this Spanish word so familiar to all of us at the time seems to have no recognized linguistic existence.

As soon as I started rummaging through my memories – in my head to start with, attempting to reconstruct a still fuzzy timeline, and to put into words any moments, images and snatches of conversation I could recall – it was the first thing I looked for. The word was inextricably linked to the fragments of Argentine childhood I was struggling to remember, and yet I had never come across it in any other context, despite hearing and saying it constantly at the time.

First, I consulted the dictionaries I happened to have at home: no trace of *embute*. During the next few months I questioned every Spanish-speaking person I came across: none of them knew the word.

Then, someone told me that it's possible to email the Real Academia Española with any kind of linguistic question. They explained that the academy responds, in a few days or at the most one or two weeks, to the queries of all Spanish-speaking people whatever their question. I was thrilled to discover this, and to be able to consult such a prestigious institution to finally get a definitive answer to my question.

I wanted to know whether the word was attested somewhere – even just as an Americanism or neologism – and also how an educated Spanish speaker might understand it. The response I received said that this form could only be 'the third person singular of the present indicative of the verb *embutir*'. And yet, at that time, in the isolated world of the Montoneros, *embute* was definitely used as a noun.

The only term with an official linguistic existence in Spanish – the Spanish of dictionaries and linguists at least – is therefore the verb *embutir*, which means 'to make sausages'. The verb does have other possible meanings: 'stuff', 'fill', 'insert' or even 'run into' (*emboutir*). Be that as it may, the primary meaning of the verb relates to the making of *saucisson* and blood sausage.

So, one might conclude that the term *embute* relates to the meat found inside the sausages (what they're stuffed with), or perhaps to the fabric encasing them (what you stuff). And yet the way I remember it, the word *embute*, as we used it, had nothing whatsoever to do with the art of sausage-making.

So I carried on looking, without recourse to specialists, searching on the internet for instances of this word on every possible Spanish-language page.

Twice, the word appeared in the sense of *embuste*, a Spanish term meaning 'trickery'. But in both cases *embute* was clearly a misspelling.

Mexicans, on the other hand, did sometimes seem to use *embute* as a common noun, but only in a sexual context, as slang. During my internet research, I found the word on a chat forum where the participants (all using pseudonyms) debated extremely technical, in-depth sexual issues. During a discussion on this erotic Mexican blog of the question '*¿Beso negro, qué es?*', someone using the name Tancredo had, barely a few weeks earlier, written: '*La palabreja* embute, *también es muy empleada por* don Nadie.' Unfortunately, the testimony of Mr Nobody was no longer accessible on the blog. As for Tancredo, he provided no further information.

I discover that other Argentines on the web do use the word in exactly the way we used it at the time, but only ever in texts about 1970s political repression in Argentina, and usually in inverted commas.

Embute seems to belong to a kind of jargon specific to the Argentine revolutionary movements of the time; it is dated now, and has clearly disappeared from the language.

8

THE REASON MY MOTHER MUSTN'T LEAVE THE house is that her photo has been published in the newspapers. Her current bright red hairstyle may be very different from the sober brown of when she actually looked like my mother, which is to say during her college years – the photo published in the newspaper *El Dia* was from that time; it must have been found in the archives of the university where she studied history – but it's still better that she keeps away from prying eyes.

Luckily, the same doesn't go for me. I still look just the same as before, but no one is searching for me. I just happen to be here, witnessing all this.

Every day, around six in the evening, I see our neighbour go past. She's a beautiful tall blonde with very long, straight hair; slim, often wearing tight trousers, and always teetering along on very high heels. A pure fantasy, to judge by the admiring gazes of the exclusively male group that always gathers on the pretext of sharing a few matés, at the exact time when the whole neighbourhood knows that our beautiful neighbour will be returning home.

I look at her, too.

It's obvious that she feels assailed by the male observers who look her over from head to foot, as connoisseurs. When there are more or bolder maté drinkers than usual, it seems to me that she casts about for a female face, or at least a gaze more kindly than famished – which is when she sees me, smiling at her with a smile that, though full of well-deserved admiration, is not grasping like those of the *materos* who have decided to display their lust without modesty or restraint.

More and more often, the two of us repeat an identical scene. Around six in the evening, from the moment when she appears at the bus stop to when she unlocks her door, two hundred metres further on, she walks looking straight ahead, making no sign that she knows she is being watched, even though everyone knows she knows, that she is perfectly aware… And whenever I'm nearby, I'm the only one to receive a complicit glance, and a smile.

How many times did this scene repeat itself before she said a word to me? Ten? Fifteen?

One day, finding me once again alone, and just as delighted to see her appear at the corner, she asks me in.

She gives me milk, and cakes, before inviting me into her room.

'Come, you can help me,' she says.

And then she opens the doors of an old wardrobe containing nothing but countless pairs of shoes.

She has shoes of every shape and every colour, but the ones that impress me most are the several pairs of pink and purple high heels – I've never seen shoes that colour before.

'Pretty, aren't they?'

I hear myself reply, 'Yes,' in a choked voice.

She says, 'You can pick them up, or touch them, if you like.'

I don't dare, in case I spoil them.

'If you like pink, come here and I'll show you something.'

She stands on a stool and pulls down a white box from the very top shelf of her wardrobe. She takes out a magnificent pair of shoes, the like of which I have never seen. They are of a pale, yet very shiny pink leather, crowned with a bow made from the same patent but decorated with pleats, as if it were cloth. The heel is rather wide and sturdy, probably to allow for its great height. When the neighbour picks up one of the shoes and I see, from underneath, the solid pink column leading up to the stiffener it holds exquisitely aloft, I realize I am witnessing the necessary and natural accessory of a princess. I'm not sure I will ever be worthy of wearing such a thing, but I am immediately proud to have been given the opportunity of seeing it up close.

She selects five or six pairs of shoes that she puts on the floor, in front of her bed. Then from another wardrobe she takes a white dress whose front is scattered with green, pink and purple dots, much bigger than normal polka dot fabric. Some of them overlap, but always in a unique way – sometimes a pink dot partially covers a green dot, other times it's the pink that is partially hidden.

All of a sudden, she asks me:

'Tell me, little one, which shoes would you wear with this dress?'

I am surprised by the question, and don't say anything for a long time. I rule out the princess shoes immediately, sensing that they could be worn only for an exceptional occasion. And in any case, there must be a reason why she has carefully put them back in their box, whose bottom is carpeted with several sheets of tissue paper.

I point at a pair of green shoes.

'You've chosen very well,' she tells me.

*

My mother bursts into the kitchen as I'm laying the table for lunch. She is furious. She stands in the doorway, as if her fury prevented her from coming any further.

'What happened with the neighbour?'

'Nothing…'

'What do you mean, nothing? What did you tell her?'

'I didn't say anything. She just showed me all her pairs of shoes.'

My mother seems to be getting more and more angry. She is clearly expecting me to confess something, but I can't see what so I burst into tears.

Diana has followed her into the kitchen, and comes towards me as she tries to calm Mama down. She starts talking to me now, in her soft, gentle voice.

'It's OK, I've managed to sort things out, she seemed to believe me. But what were you doing, telling her that you didn't have a surname?'

I can't understand what she's talking about.

She starts explaining that the neighbour came to see her this very morning to ask what was going on with 'that little girl', who told her she didn't have a surname. Diana is clearly telling the story to my mother for at least the second time.

I realize that 'that little girl' is me.

Apparently, this all took place yesterday, but I don't remember it. Or I don't remember it any more. I don't think so, anyway.

Now that Diana is telling the story, yes, it does seem to me that the neighbour asked my name, before or after the shoes, when we were in her bedroom. Before, I expect. Yes, I think she asked me. I replied, 'Laura.' I just said my first name because I know that this is the part of my name that I will be keeping. After that, I think she asked: 'And your surname?' I honestly can't remember what happened next. I must have panicked because I know that my mother is a wanted person and that we're waiting for our new surname, and our false papers. Am I a wanted person too? Yes, in some way, no doubt, although I do know that I'm here by accident.

Could I have been the daughter of an army man? No, that was impossible, unbearable, it wouldn't have been me. What about the daughter of López Rega, the 'Sorcerer'?

No, of course not, not at all, he's a perverse, cynical killer, everyone knows it, he could father nothing but monsters. And I don't think I'm a monster. So what could I say, then? What is my surname?

Yes, now that I'm trying to remember the scene, I think I was afraid, for a moment, at the neighbour's house. It may well be that I replied that I had no surname, as she told you, Diana.

But you mustn't get so angry, Mama, I can see that it was ridiculous. Not ridiculous, no, sorry, I completely understand that this is serious, very serious even. I have put us all in danger. I made a huge blunder that would render anyone suspicious – no little girl of seven years old doesn't know her own surname, or thinks it's possible not to have one. The worst thing is that I didn't mention it, didn't try to prevent this great blunder from turning into a catastrophe. Yes, why didn't I say anything, why didn't I warn you? If she had told anyone else of my gaffe, the whole neighbourhood would have started thinking we were odd. They probably already do. That's true. And so, if everyone had found out that in this house lives a seven-year-old girl who claims she doesn't have a surname, they would definitely have thought we were very, very peculiar... We really don't need, as well as the grey van's night-time excursions, and all the earth we have to get rid of, a little girl who says: 'I've no surname, my family has no surname.' You're right, Diana. Sorry, Mama.

I know I was afraid, I remember it perfectly now, I felt as if I had fallen into a trap in that house, with that magnificent blonde creature with the shoes, who kept asking me: 'But what is your surname, your family name? Nobody doesn't have a surname, you must have one! Your father and mother are Mr and Mrs what?' Yes, that's right, I remember now: 'My mother and father don't have a surname, either. They are Mr and Mrs nothing, just like me.'

My mother has gone very pale, or at least a very unusual colour, a very strange colour indeed.

As for me, I feel as if the roof is about to cave in, as if the moustachioed AAA men are already outside in their black no-number-plate cars, armed to the teeth. As if they are about to burst into the house and kill us all like rabbits at the far end of the shed, just in front of the big hole.

I am expecting something to happen immediately, something that is tragic for all of us, waiting for an imminent end to all these strange things that keep happening. Then, against all expectation, Diana bursts out laughing; a bright, joyful laugh that cuts through the unbearable heaviness that has settled in the little kitchen.

'What you said was so outrageous that it helped me provide a believable explanation. I said that your parents had split up and this was no doubt your way of expressing your grief and confusion. She seemed very moved when I told her that.'

Me too. And relieved, especially. I am so relieved that Diana thought to invent me a normal childhood trauma. She is still laughing, looking from my mother to me and back:

'It was funny, you know, I made a whole story out of it...'

And finally, turning towards me:

'I doubt she'll ever dare mention your parents again!'

9

THE LABOURER IS PUTTING THE FINISHING TOUCHES to our two building sites. He has brought me a present. To stop me from getting bored.

A kitten.

It was such a lovely surprise to see him getting out of the van with a little tabby kitten. It had travelled in his arms, under the old red blanket.

It must be a few weeks old; it's tiny and full of energy.

I love playing with my kitten.

The only problem is that he doesn't know when to calm down, when to be still. He doesn't listen when I say stop. When I want to finish playing so I can go and check on the building site at the far end of the shed, he clings to my ankles and bites me. I shake my leg, sometimes managing to dislodge him, but he always comes back.

The more I push him away, the more vicious he becomes, sometimes even taking a run and jumping up at my knee with his claws out. When the two of us get to that point he won't even look at me, won't listen to me at all. He goes at me unrelentingly, with a stupid, instinctual hostility I'm unable to shift.

Sometimes I can't stand it any more: I grab him by the tail and throw him against the courtyard wall as hard as I can, to knock him out once and for all.

But my little cat always returns to the fray.

And so I do, too, even harder than before, taking a run up, as if I were throwing a ball in a massive sports pitch. But the courtyard is small, the wall is close, and he ought to bash his brains out on the wall, which is barely two metres away.

Strangely, the little tabby cat always jumps up just as easily, hopping to the side as if propelled by some kind of spring.

And so I do it again, but these creatures really are extremely tough. I can understand the phrase *tener siete vidas como los gatos*, even if mine seems to have more than nine lives. Many more.

So death *can* be elusive.

I don't know who came up with the idea of the rabbits, if it was the Engineer, or one of the people living in the house, or whether the leaders of the organization had the idea for us. Cesar, perhaps? I definitely understood the Engineer's concept when he explained to me how things could be hidden by not hiding them. But rabbits? How was living with hundreds of rabbits going to protect us?

Cacho talked about this all through dinner today, because they will be arriving soon. He described to us what it will be like when the rabbits are here.

He explained it like this: rabbit breeding would be the house's official activity. The domestic, cottage industry part anyway because, rabbits or no rabbits, Cacho would be keeping his job in Buenos Aires. But the breeding activity would justify all the comings and goings. Just as the rabbit building site had until now justified the other, *embute* building site. Once the rabbits had arrived, the endless journeys of the grey van – which would be transporting people and distributing the newspapers we print – would be explained by the transport of rabbits and the delivery of our stews.

'Oh, will we be making stews?' I asked.

'Yes, we will… but we will eat them ourselves. We'll

pretend to fill great tubs, but in reality the tubs will contain copies of *Evita Montonera*...'

Certain things aren't very clear to me yet. I don't dare speak when I'm serving maté in a meeting, in front of Cesar, but I know that I can ask questions now, between ourselves, at dinner. It's weird, but we're a bit like a family – Cacho, Diana whose belly is growing bigger every day, my mother and me.

'And if someone comes to buy a rabbit – someone from the neighbourhood, I mean – do we open the door and let them into the house, then?'

'In principle, yes... but Argentines eat nothing but beef, so no one will come.'

*

They arrived today, in the grey van.

I couldn't say how many there were: fifty, a hundred, maybe more? In any case, it took several journeys to collect all the inhabitants of our little farm.

The cages have been stacked on top of each other, creating a motley wall of wire mesh, white fur and hundreds of pairs of red eyes, between the door into the shed and the false back wall.

The rabbits that have already been weaned are

crammed into fattening cages; there are usually six or seven to a tiny compartment. The mummy rabbits are slightly better off, important enough to have a whole cage to themselves.

I like to watch them crowding around the water pipette, or eating sand-coloured granules while my mother works a little rotary press just behind the false back wall. You see, the rabbits arrived at the same time as the press began to print in earnest.

At the end of the shed is a huge stack of carefully folded newspapers. The copies of *Evita Montonera* are wrapped in packs of ten and neatly arranged in staggered rows to form strange-looking columns. In front of the false back wall, the rabbits are multiplying at an extraordinary rate. And the more balls of white fur inhabit the cages, the more deeply my mother's hands are stained with thick black ink. Soon she won't be able to get rid of it, even by scrubbing very hard with white soap and a little hard-bristled brush.

*

Today, we did our first culinary experiment.

Diana caught a pretty white rabbit by its ears, intending to kill it 'nice and quick'.

The rabbit seemed to know what was coming and

struggled fiercely, glaring at Diana with its scarlet eyes. She wedged it against the kitchen worktop and asked me to hold down its back feet.

'It's very simple. Everyone knows you just have to give them a little whack at the back of the head.'

Diana told me that she'd read this in a book, or else someone had told her, she couldn't quite remember. This was a first for her too.

With great enthusiasm, she grabbed the little wooden hammer we used for tenderizing meat cutlets, and gave the rabbit a whack behind the head. The hammer bounced off the thick white fur covering what seemed to be the nape of its neck. The rabbit struggled even harder, trying to escape with more and more determination.

'I can't understand why people don't like eating rabbit in this country,' said Diana, not at all fazed by the failure of her first attempt. 'Perhaps it's down to the phrase *vender gato por liebre*. Apparently, once it's on a plate you can't tell the difference between cat, hare and rabbit meat. But you'll know this isn't your little cat, because we'll have killed it together.'

As she said these words, the rabbit's efforts to escape got the better of me; its back feet slipped out of my hands and it managed to get away for a few moments until Diana caught it by the ears again and squashed its legs back down against the tiled worktop. Holding it firmly, she added:

'But I can't imagine people often get conned in that way; it must be much harder to kill a cat. If we were trying to kill a cat, now, it would have already leapt at our faces with its claws out…'

I nodded my head, ashamed of my lapse in concentration, which had almost scuppered our first attempt. Forcing myself to be up to the task, I added:

'I've got it, now. I won't let go, I'm holding it very hard with both hands.'

Diana looked at me suddenly:

'The problem is that you're much too small. If you were looking down on the rabbit, like me, you could lean on him with your whole body weight.'

As she said this she pulled a stool towards me, using one of her feet as a hook. I was amazed at how agile she was, despite her big pregnant belly. At the same time, she was holding down the head and front legs of the rabbit, which was still struggling.

'Here you are, step up onto it.'

I kept hold of my bit of the rabbit, too, while I stepped up onto the stool.

'How's that?' asked Diana.

'Yes, it's much better like this. I won't let it go.'

'Good, excellent. Although I do think there's also a problem with our utensil. I had thought the cutlet hammer would do... Hold him tight, now, while I fetch the cast-iron pan.'

While I held the rabbit, crushing its paws down onto the tiles, Diana managed to administer the fatal blow. After a few convulsive jolts, the rabbit finally stopped moving.

*

Then Cacho had another idea. One day at breakfast he just said, apropos of nothing:

'If there's a police roadblock, they might open the tubs to check our stews, and come across the newspapers.'

Diana, my mother and I looked at each other, surprised more than anything. Of course the danger was great. Massive, even. What was he getting at, stating the obvious like this first thing in the morning?

'What about gift-wrapping them? Big parcels wrapped in shiny paper with lots of coloured ribbon? No one would hesitate to open a tub just for the hell of it, but any policeman would think twice before destroying a pretty present wrapped with love, especially if Diana was driving, don't you think?'

We all laughed as we looked at her. She was laughing, too, amused, tilting her head this way and that to look even more like a sweet, charming young girl. With her big pregnant belly, lovely eyes and pretty blonde curls, it was easy to imagine her passing through any roadblock with a huge beribboned parcel in the back of her van. And even receiving a warm smile from the policeman. Then, nodding his head at me, Cacho added:

'And the little one could help with the parcels. You'd like to make pretty parcels full of copies of *Evita Montonera*, wouldn't you?'

'Yeah! It would be fun! Could I curl the ribbons like they do in the big shops?'

'You bet! We'll make gorgeous parcels, just you wait and see. It's a bit like what the Engineer explained to you about the *embute*, that you found so strange, do you remember? Instead of hiding our newspapers, we'll tie them up in ribbons. The police won't suspect a thing!'

10

AFTER DISCUSSING IT IN A MEETING AT THE house, they have decided that I will go to school, but to a private school called San Cayetano where they've heard that the police hardly ever check pupil identity. They all think that my false papers, which we have only just received, are more likely to go unnoticed there.

*

The classes are taught by nuns, and the pupils are all little girls.

All these little girls together – it's so sad.

The worst is at break time. The lack of boys is very oppressive. Like a coating of lead, dooming us to boredom and horribly tame games with predictable outcomes.

The little girls are all so well behaved. There's a bit of life in each of us individually, but put us all in the San Cayetano playground and it's as if our individual energies cancel each other out. At break time we wander around in silent, gloomy herds. There are quite a lot of us, but the playground still suffocates in unbearable silence.

The nuns also move around silently, in twos and threes, barely looking at us we're so well behaved or, if they do, with dull, lacklustre eyes. As if their eyes just slip over us.

Then a bell rings from somewhere, and we get into class groups, two by two, well-ordered little rows of white blouses facing the door of our classroom and the nun who serves as our teacher.

I can't tell what colour hair our nun has – Rosa, her name is – because like all the others she covers it with a white-bordered black veil. To go with her long grey dress. But I imagine her blonde because she has blue eyes – not that she ever looks at us.

When we are let into the classroom, each little girl walks to the place she has been assigned. We stand up nice and straight, arms hanging at our sides, as Rosa steps up onto a platform and takes the same stance as us, waiting motionless for a long moment next to her desk. What is she waiting for? Not for silence, no. The silence is constant.

Then she clasps her hands, closes her eyes and, bending her head very slightly as if apologizing for breaking the silence, intones: '*Padre nuestro que estás en el cielo...*' All the little girls echo her, striving to say each syllable of the prayer at the same time as Rosa, and making sure not to drown out her voice with ours. And she doesn't pray at all loudly, so we have to keep our voices to a murmur. And then it's back to silence. We all keep our heads bent and hands joined; we know it's not over yet. Soon Rosa continues, in her reedy, pure, monotonous voice: '*Dios te salve, Maria...*' And we all follow, still restraining ourselves to an almost imperceptible volume.

And again, silence.

In response to the subtlest of hand gestures we sit down, gently lifting our chairs as we do, lest their movement should bother anyone's delicate ears. Twenty-five chairs move without a whisper. At San Cayetano, everything must happen in silence. If someone were to witness this scene with their eyes closed, they would definitely think that nothing at all had taken place in the little classroom.

Then Rosa makes another movement with her hand, a gesture that seems a mirror image of the previous one: having moved her right hand towards the window facing the street, while very slightly turning her palm towards it, she is now turning her palm the other way, as if seeking to erase the first movement. We all sit down at the same time, all equally docile and meek.

Still on the platform, Rosa now moves behind her desk and, with her hands resting upon it, starts declaiming something. I'm not sure what exactly, but she talks and talks, looking straight ahead, her eyes empty.

I wonder whether her veil is itchy.

And then it's break time again, even more interminable than before.

Endless.

On the way home, I always stop by a ditch. I've got a little see-through flask and I like to put tadpoles in it.

After that I go home for tea.

Today is the day for cleaning weapons. I try to find a clean corner of table that isn't strewn with oil-covered rods and swabs. I don't want my bread and *dulce de leche* getting dirty.

11

YESTERDAY I WENT TO VISIT MY FATHER IN
prison, for the second time.

This is how it happened: my mother and I left the
rabbit house very early in the morning, and took a bus to
the city centre. We got off the bus next to a square that I
think I was seeing for the first time yesterday. My paternal
grandmother and grandfather were sitting on a bench, a
little way from the play area in the middle of the square.
They and my mother barely said a few words to each
other, simply confirming the time and place of another
rendezvous, that same evening. Then my mother walked
away, leaving me with them, having given them my identity card from before, the one with my real name, the one
I used before my brand-new false papers.

We got into grandfather's car. We waited until there was no one in the square or the surrounding streets, but not many people are out at that time of the morning so we didn't have to wait long. Then my grandfather turned towards me and pressed down very gently on my head:

'Lie down, and cover yourself with that blanket on the seat.'

That was all he had to say – I knew what to do.

Then my grandmother started speaking to me, without turning around, as I lay in the back under the blanket. Her voice suddenly seemed very weak and muffled – not only was she facing another direction, but also, lying on my belly under the blanket, I was squeezing my head as hard as I could between my arms. And yet I still managed to make out a few words:

'*Tula… contenta…*'

I didn't ask for any explanations. I didn't know where we were, or where we were going. I didn't move, forcing myself to keep as still and silent as, I was sure, the Engineer and the Labourer did every time they hid under the old blanket in Diana's van.

After quite a while I noticed the engine stop, and then my grandmother set me free.

'Here we are, at the house.'

It took me a while to recognize the place, which was completely plunged in darkness. I stayed sitting on the back seat, dazed, waiting for someone to come and get me.

My grandmother stepped out of the car first, and opened the door for me. At that point I recognized my grandparents' garage.

'See, she was waiting for you.'

It was Tula, the dog I had been given four or five years earlier and who had stayed with my grandparents because things were complicated enough already. She was running around and around me, wagging her tail. Happy. How weird, that she had recognized me. As if I were still the same.

*

The dining room in my grandparents' house is very small. The table is wedged against the wall, under a window looking out over the courtyard.

We eat *matambre* and salad in silence. I don't dare speak, and neither do they.

They don't ask me a single question, not about where I live, nor about my new school.

I am strangely relieved.

Tula's delight, her enthusiasm. So unexpected, and so reassuring.

I lie down on my back, with my arms stretched out sideways, and she comes over to me. I close my eyes and turn my head from side to side as Tula licks my face.

*

We leave again, with me once more hidden under the blanket, but less tense this time. After a few minutes, my grandmother touches my head and says:

'You can come out now. We're nearly at the prison.'

I obey, but I'm very anxious:

'But they'll see me, the police…'

'We didn't want the neighbours to… Questions, you know… As for the police, if someone asks what you're doing here, we'll say that you were left on our doorstep. If anyone asks you anything, this is what you should say: that you were in a place you didn't know, with strangers whose names you didn't know, and then someone just abandoned you on our doorstep. But let's hope that no one does ask any questions.'

I understand then that if anyone at the prison starts asking questions, I won't be able to return to the rabbit house. It seems to me that I'm afraid of this. Or at the very least, it's another thing I'm unsure about.

*

What happens next is also familiar to me. First the men and women form separate queues, to be frisked. Then the same little room, and a lady − but is she the same one? − wearing a severe suit, again with a very tight chignon perched on the top of her head. She searches us thoroughly, starting with my grandmother. My grandmother still has the same saggy, flabby breasts, but this time I know what to expect. Then the lady kneads and palpates us both, returning three times to my grandmother's enormous bosoms. It's true that they do seem more like sacks than breasts, and it's hard to believe that nothing but flesh is lurking in all that bulk.

In the end, the chignon lady says:

'That's fine, you can get dressed now.'

Another lady takes us to a hall where my grandfather is waiting for us on a bench, next to another man; from now on we'll be in family groups. Then a first gate is opened by a pot-bellied policeman, and we walk down a very long, windowless corridor.

At the end of this corridor there's another gate and another portly policeman, very like the first, with oily black hair and an equally black moustache, made shiny by grease. We are frisked again, but briefly this time and without having to undress, as this is in full view of everyone. I wonder what the point is, after the long palpating by the chignon lady.

In front of us is a grey metal door, with a tiny opening at the very top, covered with a row of tight little bars. A soldier is standing on either side of the door. Each of them holds a massive firearm, a far more serious weapon than those held by the portly policemen. The barrels seem to have been well oiled – I find myself right in front of a black hole, and I can see how shiny it is. These soldiers stand motionless while another policeman opens the door and lets us through.

In the room, there are two benches facing each other, and four armed soldiers posted at each corner of the room, just like the ones on the other side of the door. Opposite us is a door identical to the one we entered through.

There are people who seem to have arrived before us, and are already sitting on the benches: a man and a woman and then, a little way away but still on the same bench, an extremely young woman with a very pink baby in her arms. The portly policeman who accompanied us into the room signals to us to sit down at one end of the bench, the same distance from the woman and child.

We wait impatiently, listening out for the clinking of

keys or the sound of footsteps. Several times we hear people approaching, but they don't stop.

In the end it's through the other door, not the one we used, that we see them come in. There are three of them, my father and two much older men. One of them has lost two front teeth – the top ones – creating another hole I find it impossible to ignore. All three men are wearing the same blue outfit my father wore on our first visit.

As soon as he walks in, my father starts smiling an embarrassed smile. I think he feels awkward at seeing me, surprised, too, and probably anxious. He sits down facing us, on the opposite bench, exactly where a new portly policeman has indicated – each prisoner has his own policeman who accompanies him and likewise shows him where he must sit.

My grandmother speaks to our one:

'Can the child hug her father?'

He looks about him, right and left, clearly not knowing the answer. The soldiers in each corner are unruffled, the barrels of their guns still pointing to the middle of the room. Obviously disconcerted and confused, the police-man shrugs his shoulders, which my grandmother quickly interprets as consent.

'The man said yes,' she says. 'Go on.'

I take a few steps towards my father with my eyes glued to the nearest gun, belonging to the man just in front of me. I am acutely aware that the black hole is exactly at the level of my head. I look up at the man but he remains motionless, the gun still pointed in front of him, betraying no reaction to either my grandmother's suggestion or my approach. After a short pause, I take a few more steps.

'Go on, then,' says my grandmother. 'Don't be scared; the man has no objection. Isn't that right, sir?'

The paunchy moustachioed man still looks as if he's seeking approval, a response; a little more anxiously, it seems to me, than before. But in vain. The soldiers with their big guns remain absolutely still.

A few more steps and suddenly I find myself gulping, retching, struggling to contain an unexpected, powerful nausea. My stomach is convulsing madly, but I manage to take a few more steps and grab hold of one of my father's dark blue sleeves. As I reach him, I vomit in his ear.

*

Then it's the return journey.

Once again I hide under the blanket, not so that I don't see where we're going, like the Engineer and the Labourer, but because my grandmother wants to protect me from the neighbours and their questions, and to protect herself as well.

I play with the dog again, who licks my face once more. And when it's dark we leave my grandparents' house and go to find my mother, somewhere in La Plata.

The exchange between my mother and my grandparents is brief: everyone has been extremely tense. As long as the situation remains as it is, I had better not visit my father in prison.

It's much too dangerous.

12

I COULD NEVER HAVE IMAGINED THE SADNESS OF a school playground without boys. At San Cayetano you never hear a shout, or a fight. The little girls wander around in a kind of daze, inert, letting themselves be led by the movements of the amorphous whole, the gloomy mass of white blouses surrounding them.

And yet today something happened, just before the end of break; something that disturbed the flow of these dreary little groupings.

Two girls abandoned their gang, stopped following their group around, and went off by themselves to a corner of the playground. The youngest of them knelt before the other, a girl with long blonde hair who must have been nine or ten years old.

Then the elder girl took a big cloth handkerchief out of the pocket of her school pinafore and put it on her head, looking straight ahead, pretending to ignore the kneeling child, who at that point joined her hands together, exactly as Rosa does every day at prayer time.

A nun scuttled over from the other end of the playground:

'What on earth are you doing? What's got into you?'

'We're playing Virgin Mary,' replied the smaller girl, still on her knees. 'Leonor is Mary, and so I'm kneeling in front of the Virgin Mary.'

She seemed very proud of her explanation, but the nun furiously snatched the white handkerchief from Leonor's head and yanked the other child up by the arm. The younger girl started shouting:

'But she's the Virgin Mary!'

The nun slapped the little girl's cheek so hard that the sound rang right across the usually silent playground.

'This is most serious, very serious indeed! No one has the right to play the Virgin Mary! No one, do you hear!'

The headmistress, a rather wrinkled, ancient nun, came charging into the playground accompanied by another nun. They all clustered together and talked among themselves, looking very agitated.

Then, the headmistress took Leonor's handkerchief and put it in her pocket, as evidence.

13

La Plata, 24 March 1976

'THAT'S IT. IT'S HAPPENED.'

It was Diana who told me, when I got up. To tell the truth, we had been expecting it for a long time.

A few days earlier, the newspapers had announced that it was imminent. One even ran the headline: '*Es imminente el final. Está todo dicho.*'

I think the people around me have been saying the same thing, although for them of course it would have a different meaning. As for me, I couldn't wait to find out which army would be in charge, and which of the candidate dictators would gain the upper hand.

'Actually, there are three of them: Videla, Massera and Agosti. Each of them is in charge of one of the military corps: the army, the navy and the air force. They've shared things out like that.'

We had known that Isabel Perón was no longer running things, and that the military were behind the deaths and disappearances, that they had been pulling the strings for a long time. And that Isabel was merely a ridiculous puppet.

The Sorcerer, López Rega, had fled a long time ago. Isabel had stayed, but seemed completely out of her depth. People were even saying that, before he left, the Sorcerer had destroyed her few remaining brain cells. He had been an evil leech on Isabel, who so wanted to be like Evita but was no more than a grotesque caricature. A pitiful, failed impersonator. This was what Diana said, and everyone agreed with her: when he died, Perón left the country in the hands of a pathetic little lady manipulated by murderers. Which is why things were as they were, and why the Montoneros had to take up arms before the coup d'état. Now at least things were clear.

Isabel's pathetic performance thus came to an end during the night of the 23rd to the 24th of March 1976, when the helicopter that was supposed to take her to the Olivos presidential residence deposited her in prison instead: her pilot was in cahoots with the instigators of the coup d'état. *La Presidenta* had been made a fool of, outmanoeuvred to the very end.

'See, the military got rid of her easily, without needing

to fire a single shot. For a long time now, what has been posing as authority has been nothing but masquerade.'

With this new junta, the military were simply taking the reins officially. Far from being a surprise, the coup d'état of March 24th was actually a kind of clarification of the situation. This is what they would write in *Evita Montonera*.

'It won't be so easy to get rid of us, I'm afraid,' said Diana, with her hands on her belly.

Then she showed me one of the photos that had just been published:

'Look. Do you see them? The most powerful and dangerous is the one in the middle, with the big black moustache. Videla. Although the other two are no angels.'

The army's plan is to 'get the country back on its feet'. 'Faced with a terrible void in leadership', Videla, Massera and Agosti felt themselves 'duty-bound, as a result of careful reflection' to 'permanently uproot the vices afflicting the country'. This is what they declared. 'With the help of God', they hoped to achieve a 'national recovery'. They even said this: 'Our task will be undertaken with absolute rigour, and a passion for service.'

We hadn't expected anything less.

14

THE ENGINEER HAS COME AROUND TO SEE IF everything is working OK.

He sits next to me and tightens a few screws on the box we use to operate the *embute*. His hands are covered in thick black oil, so he stands up by pushing his chair out with his bum and accidentally knocks off the blazer I'd hung on the back when I came home from school.

All of a sudden, he turns deathly pale.

'What does that say, on the inside of your blazer, just there?'

I pick it up. I hadn't even noticed there was something written on the inside label, in felt-tip pen. I read it and go pale myself.

'It's my uncle's name. My grandmother gave me the blazer. It was too small for him, so...'

The Engineer starts shouting. He is in a rage.

'Goddammit! This kid will get you all shot! The organization is killing itself to provide you with credible false papers, and she's going to school in a blazer with her uncle's name written all over it in black marker pen! Her uncle's *real* name! What the hell are you playing at!'

'Don't get so upset,' says Diana, 'the child knows exactly what's going on, she's very careful...'

The Engineer is more and more furious; he's shouting and spluttering above my head.

'She knows what's going on? Are you having a laugh? If she knew what was going on, if she had even the faintest idea of what is taking place in this country, she would never have screwed up like that! Fucking hell, you could at least keep a bit of an eye on her things, if she can't do it!'

Then, turning towards me:

'What would you have said if a nun had asked you why there's a name on your jacket that isn't your own? Huh? What would you have said?'

I can't speak. I look at the Engineer, petrified. I wish I could stop staring at him like this, but I can't turn my head away. It's as if I'm riveted to his gaze. I wish he would calm down, but I do understand that what I've done is very serious. I am most definitely not up to the job.

'How would you have explained it, huh? Go on, speak! What would you have told the nuns at San Cayetano?'

I can feel Diana looking at me, from the other end of the room. They are both waiting for something. I know I must answer correctly, to show that I've understood, and that if there were to be a problem I could handle it. The Engineer is screaming now:

'What would you have said? Shit! Tell me!'

There is a good reply to the question, I'm sure of it. Like all problems, this one has a solution. But my brain won't work. My head feels like a big empty ball. Hollow. I have become nothing.

After a long silence, I hear myself whisper:

'Er... I don't know... I don't know... I don't know what I would have done.'

The Engineer is still holding his hands out in front of him, fingers stretched wide so as not to rub the oil in any deeper. He kicks the chair, violently. It falls over. Then he opens the kitchen door with another kick, so as not to smear black oil all over the door handle.

'This has got to stop! Enough is enough! This is war, for Christ's sake, this is war!'

I am definitely not up to the job.

That same evening, the decision is taken: I will no longer be attending San Cayetano.

15

A WHOLE NEIGHBOURHOOD WAS CORDONED OFF this morning, just a few streets from our house. This is so that the police can go into the houses and rummage through them, inch by inch, one after the other. They do that sometimes. There's never any way of knowing how long these checks will last. You can never know, either, whether they will stick to the area initially cordoned off, or extend the search nearby. Or perhaps a little further away.

It seems that we've been lucky – we're not inside that area, which is slightly closer to the city centre. In fact, it's the bit between the city centre and us that the police have been turning upside down, and no one can be sure that they won't make it as far as the rabbit house.

Cesar came to warn us. He left again straightaway, just in case. The searches may be happening a little way away, but you can never be sure so it's better for us to be alone, to avoid putting more people in danger if there is a problem. Cacho left for Buenos Aires this morning, as he does every day. The Labourer didn't come today. As for the Engineer, we never see him any more.

The only people in the house are Diana, seven months pregnant, my mother behind the false back wall, and me.

Oh, and the rabbits. And the rolls of wrapping paper and ribbon. And the secret printing press and hundreds of copies of a banned newspaper. And also the weapons, for self-defence.

And the ferocious kitten.

We are very afraid.

After a few moments' thought, Diana decides that the best way to ready ourselves is to hide as much as we can, and forget about the weapons. We don't really have much choice.

It takes a few minutes to collect up anything that might be compromising and stuff it all into the *embute*. Women, white rabbits and a hiding place hidden by the excessively obvious. The moment may have come to put all this to the test. For real.

So that we are not caught off guard, Diana asks me to go to buy bread, and at the same time check for anything suspicious – police cars, or unfamiliar vehicles containing several people.

'If you see several men in one car, even if they're not in uniform, come and warn us. If they aren't in uniform, and it is them, then the situation really is serious.'

Outside, I see nothing suspicious.

On the pavement opposite, a little girl is skipping rope. A yellow dog is crossing the road.

So I go to buy bread.

In the bakery, an old lady is buying those little black cakes that look as if they've been forgotten in the oven and burnt. But it's brown sugar that makes them look like that, the colour is on purpose. Spluttering, her lips trembling, the lady asks the saleswoman for a kilo of *tortitas negras*.

Then it's my turn and I ask for bread, bread that we don't need. As I was told.

On my way back, the little girl has gone.

Now there's only a fat lady wearing a flowery dress, sweeping the pavement in front of her door. I can't hear anything unusual. I can't see anything that should put us on the alert.

But I don't want to go straight back to the house.

I don't want to.

So I decide to go to the scrubland beyond the opposite pavement, a few metres from the house, and pick a little bunch of grass and wild flowers for our rabbits.

At one edge of the scrubland, a short stretch of wall is still standing. It's full of holes through which the odd clump of grass has grown. There are a few piles of rubble on the ground, surrounded by tall grasses. In one corner I recognize the shoots of wild fennel that Diana once pointed out to me. I try to pick off a few shoots, but I pull too hard and the whole plant ends up in my hand, ripped from the soil by its roots. I look for the little blue flowers that Diana and I made such a pretty bouquet from last time. In vain.

There are no more blue flowers.

So I go back to the house.

'I didn't see anything,' I tell Diana.

16

I BARELY LEAVE THE HOUSE ANY MORE, APART from when Diana asks me to get a few things from the local shops.

We spend long hours at the kitchen table, wrapping hundreds of copies of *Evita Montonera* in the new red and gold paper Cacho has brought back from Buenos Aires. Diana cuts up the paper and I curl short lengths of coloured ribbon. I prefer it to the paper cutting. I try to shape them into big fat flowers, but Diana keeps restraining my artistic impulses.

'That's pretty, but don't use so much. We're already on our third roll of red ribbon. Look how many papers we've still got to wrap... that's enough, with the ribbon. If you don't want to cut the paper, you can stick on the greetings labels.'

My mother never sets foot outside any more. I hardly see her inside either, apart from at meal times. Since the coup d'état, the offset rotary press hidden behind the rabbit cages has been printing as many papers as possible, and my mother doesn't have a moment's rest. So I spend most of my time wrapping parcels with Diana, and chatting with her about the military and the war. And the child who will soon be born.

*

When the doorbell rang, Diana was frightened, too. We weren't expecting anyone: Cacho usually arrived back from Buenos Aires much later, and Cesar wasn't due to visit that day.

When I heard it ring, I rushed up to Diana and followed a few steps behind her, incapable of staying in the kitchen by myself. I could see how pale she was. I knew that the army could turn up at any moment and that the weapons in the *embute* were for precisely that situation, if our act should fail to convince.

Diana drew back her bedroom curtain a fraction, hoping to see who was at the door.

'I think it's for you,' she said, apparently reassured.

She walked to the front door.

For a moment, I was even more frightened. I clung to her dress with both hands, hiding behind her, walking in her footsteps. I think I was trying to get as close to her as physically possible. I would perhaps have liked her to pick me up. I think what I really wanted was to copy her movements to the extent of melting, disappearing into her. Then I said to myself that if it was only for me, it couldn't be that. Not yet. No, it couldn't be that.

'I was wondering, could the little girl come over to my place sometimes? Is she in?'

I showed myself then, taking a step to the side. I had recognized the neighbour's voice. She was still just as beautiful. Still just as blonde.

'Would you like to come over?'

I was unable to say a word. Luckily, Diana replied for me.

'Of course she would. You would, wouldn't you?'

I nodded my head, still silent. Yes, I would, I would like to very much. She couldn't imagine how much.

*

And then the moments of respite became rare. The fear was everywhere. Especially in that house.

I no longer had the slightest faith that the white rabbits would protect us. What a joke! And as for the ribbons...

Each week, Cacho brought back bits of news that weren't always published in the newspapers. Montoneros being killed on a daily basis; entire networks disappearing. Although some were killed openly in the street, more frequently the militants just disappeared. Vanished.

So when Diana asked me if I wanted to go with her in the grey van to deliver some newspapers, I was very happy and, most of all, very relieved. That house was the scariest place. When I think of my mother, walled up behind the rabbits, working the rotary press... But that day, thankfully, Diana and I were able to go out for a little while.

Diana put a pretty parcel on the back seat, decorated with lots of red ribbon and an enormous *Felicidades!* label. Then she started the grey van, and we headed towards the city centre.

Like most meetings, this one took place in a La Plata square, where a hook-up is more likely to go unnoticed. We were meeting a woman who would be accompanied by a little girl of about my age. I had never seen her before, but I smiled at her and she immediately returned my smile. She was probably in the same sort of situation as me. In any case, I could tell just by looking at her that she was also living in fear. I knew the fear would still be there after-wards, and for as long as all this lasted, but meeting this girl was a comfort to me. That day, it was as if the two of us were able to share the burden of our fear – which was bound to make it feel a little less heavy.

Once we'd given the parcel to the lady, we got back into our car.

'They tortured that woman, but she didn't talk. Horrible things were done to her, you know, things one doesn't describe to a little girl of your age. But she didn't open her mouth. She endured the whole thing without a word.'

I didn't try to find out what those 'things' were. I know how to keep quiet, too.

I just imagined them.

I thought of things that hurt a great, great deal, things with big rusty nails or lots of little knives hidden inside them. And the woman, who didn't open her mouth. And then I thought, deep inside, that to be a strong woman was to keep quiet like that.

17

HOW LONG IS IT THAT I HAVEN'T BEEN GOING TO school? Three months, or perhaps four. It was my own fault that it became impossible for me to go back to the nuns. In any case the subject is never even mentioned now.

I am haunted by the possibility of becoming stupid, like *La Presidenta*, who by the end really didn't know what was going on. They gradually emptied her brain. The Sorcerer, in particular, demolished her remaining brain cells by organizing magic rituals supposed to increase her charisma and help her take Evita's place in the hearts of the Argentine people.

There may not be anyone as sinister as him around me, but I know that I should be learning new things and that all these school-less days are taking me further and further away from other children, and from what's going on outside. Even though I don't remember a word of Rosa's declamations at San Cayetano, now that I'm no longer at school I feel as if I miss them. And even the silent playground, and the well-behaved little girls.

So in the evenings, when we've finished our parcels, I sometimes get out the little exercise book I took to the nuns, in which I managed to write down a few of the lessons. I try to pick them back up, and carry on by myself, but I don't really know how.

Sometimes, Diana tries to teach me a little. Just before she starts cooking, she makes up a few questions for me to solve at the kitchen table, before I lay it for our evening meal. Usually, she has me do maths.

I especially love it when she makes up story questions, like the time the inhabitants of a village had to share out a 250kg bag of flour. They had to do it fairly – 5kg per adult and 2.5 per child, but they also had to keep some back for the village school, 30 or 40kg, I can't remember exactly, and so I had to work out how many children the village had, and how many adults, once she had told me that there were one and a half times as many children as adults.

As a final challenge, Diana asked me to illustrate the question with a multicoloured drawing.

*

One day, I told Diana that I wanted to make up questions, too, like she did with the maths ones, and what did she think of me inventing some crosswords? She said:

'Crosswords? Yes, that could be good practice. Sure, go ahead, I'll correct them for you.'

I decided to surprise her, by thinking up a crossword that reflected something of what we were going through.

It was really strange doing it in the exercise book they had bought me for San Cayetano, where I had to hide everything and not say a word, but I knew that it didn't matter any more, that I would never be going back; I was even sure that the exercise book would never again leave the house. Here is the crossword I made up:

HORIZONTAL CLUES

1. *Del verbo 'ir'*: VA
2. *Imitadora fracasada y odiada*: ISABEL
3. *Del verbo 'dar'*: DA
4. *Patria o…*: MUERTE

VERTICAL CLUES

1. *Asesino*: VIDELA
2. *Casualidad*: ASAR
3. *Literatura, música*: ARTE

I found myself with a flawed, embryonic grid, full
of blanks or else too many black squares. In any case, I
really didn't know what to do next; I had ground to a
halt.

Diana noticed that I hadn't written anything for a few
minutes and came to look over my shoulder at what I'd
done. First of all she smiled. I was very happy; I might be
struggling to finish, but I hadn't completely blown it. Then
she played at being teacher:

'You've made a spelling mistake, here. Spelled like that,
asar is a verb in the infinitive. It means "to cook" or "to
roast"; it's the root of the word *asado*, which is also written
with an *s*. The word you were thinking of is the common
noun meaning "chance event or situation". But it's spelled
with a *z*.'

My grid was shaky enough as it was, and now it had a spelling mistake...

Azar: the second vertical word was worthy of its name – it was only there by chance. The other words were the ones I'd chosen to make Diana laugh, especially the fourth horizontal clue PATRIA O MUERTE (patriotism or death), which Firmenich always signed off with, and which concluded the most important articles in *Evita Montonera*. I had often seen it daubed on the walls of the city, when I still used to take the bus. I even remember once, a long time ago, I think it was before my father went to prison, seeing a wall inscribed with PATRIA O MU. I'm not sure who I was with, one of my aunts perhaps. But I clearly remember that person saying to me: 'Look, how funny, a Montonero militant must have been caught before he could finish his graffiti. But actually, perhaps it's better like that, less scary anyway: if we don't look after our country, we will all become great big cows, muuu!'

That really made me laugh. It's also why I remember the slogan so well. PATRIA O MUUUHH! I preferred that, personally, but Diana wouldn't have understood because she probably never saw that unfinished graffiti.

Anyway, just like the first and third horizontal words, *azar* had ended up there without me particularly choosing it – just to fill a few more blanks and make it look more like a crossword.

But when Diana pointed out my mistake, I knew immediately that I had to keep the word, to protect it.

I decided to correct my second horizontal clue, even if it meant altering the spelling of the 'hateful, pathetic copy-cat'. At least then my grid wouldn't be wrong:

HORIZONTAL CLUES

2. *Imitadora fracasada y odiada (con una falta de ortografía)*: IZABEL

18

I REMEMBER SEVERAL MEETINGS TAKING PLACE AT the house soon after that, all presided over by Cesar, and much closer together than usual.

It was during one of these meetings that a new subject came up. Our departure.

It turned out that my mother had managed to meet up with her father, the lawyer who defended small-time smugglers and drug dealers. Terrified by what was going on, by all these deaths and disappearances – there were more every day – he said he would do everything possible to get us out of the country.

'Yes, but your father isn't one of us. Does he want to donate money to the organization?'

I continue serving the maté, though not to Cesar. He

takes it with sugar and everyone else prefers it bitter, so I serve him last because after he's sweetened it the maté is no good for anyone else, and I have to make a new gourd.

'He wants us to leave – the child and me. He's not remotely trying to help the organization. He's a Peronist through and through, but old-school Peronist – traditional and pretty right-wing. Having said that, he's no *gorila*, he doesn't support the junta.'

I keep quietly serving the maté, but I don't miss a word of the conversation and I feel greatly reassured by what I have just heard. I adore him anyway, but a *gorila* for a grandfather, now that would have been tough...

My mother continues: 'My departure could be useful to us... I could help from abroad. Lots of militants have already left, haven't they? It's important to denounce what's happening here, in Europe.'

'You're right, lots of militants have already left. But not the grassroots, just the leaders, *la conducción*.'

There's silence, an uncomfortable, discomforting silence...

What did he say? Is it true?

Are grassroots militants getting killed while their leaders seek safety abroad?

Cesar looks as if he wishes he hadn't just said that. As

if he's suddenly realized everything that his comment might suggest.

'In any case, we need your daughter to explain how she's become as thick as thieves with the gorgeous blonde next door. Because she's the only one who's managed to get that close...'

Everyone bursts out laughing.

Without much conviction.

*

The third or fourth time the subject was raised, a decision was taken. To tell the truth, I can't really remember how many times the issue was brought up for discussion, perhaps it took more meetings than that, but I remember clearly that one day Cesar made the following declaration:

'We accept that you will leave with your daughter. But we won't do anything to assist you. The organization won't give you any money, as it does with members of *la conducción*. You won't receive help of any kind from us. If you leave we'll spare you, but you'll be on your own.'

I walked up to Cesar, holding the maté and the kettle.

'I'm about to change the *yerba*. Shall I serve you a little sweetened maté?'

'Yes, that's kind of you...'

He was silent for a moment, uneasy.

He drank his maté very slowly, pausing several times, until we all heard the characteristic whistle the *bombilla* makes when there's no water left in the gourd. Eventually, speaking quietly and looking at the floor, he added:

'Our people are dying every day. They are massacring us. We can keep fighting, we have to keep believing, but… I am not going to stop you leaving if you've got the opportunity… so…'

After a long sigh – as if he'd had to search for his breath far, far away, deep inside – he added:

'Let's discuss the method now. It's better if the child leaves the room.'

'But shouldn't I serve you another maté?'

'No, that's OK, I can manage on my own,' he added, with a laugh that defused the atmosphere.

EPILOGUE

THIS IS HOW WE LEFT.

My mother was helped out of the country by one of the men my grandfather knew so well, and who in turn knew the border between Argentina, Paraguay and Brazil (where the three countries meet) like the back of his hand. It was his way of thanking my grandfather for an old favour. In this way, my mother was able to leave Argentina and then Latin America, and find refuge in France. I, on the other hand, travelled much later. My mother had had no choice, no option but to flee the country in secret; my grandfather wanted me to leave overtly and legally. With a father in prison and a mother on the run, this took a long time and was somewhat complicated.

At my grandparents' place we managed to keep hold of the new bathtub, but I lived there long enough to see more than one ashtray and quite a few musical boxes go astray… And yet, we had all been shown that, when it mattered, some of my grandfather's clients were capable of returning favours in royal style. So, full respect to them! And too bad for the ashtrays and fiddled locks!

Interestingly, I have no memories at all of saying goodbye to Diana and Cacho. It was a very difficult time, politically, but perhaps we marked the occasion with a rabbit dinner?

I do remember that Diana was about to give birth. I can still see myself telling her how sad I am to leave before the child is born. Later, I found out that she and Cacho had a little girl, Clara Anahí, born on 12 August 1976.

As for what happened after we left, the news trickled through to me in dribs and drabs over the years – and in a very muddled way.

Years later, well after the return to democracy, my father – who had been freed a long time ago: like many political prisoners he was let out of prison a few months before the Falklands War, as the dictatorship started to crumble – gave me a book, saying: 'Here, this book mentions the house you lived in with your mother.'

That was all he said. It's very difficult for us to talk about that time.

The name of the book is *Los del 73, Memoria Montonera*. It's an account written by two old militants, Gonzalo Leonidas Chaves and Jorge Omar Lewinger. I looked for the passage my father had referred to when he gave me the book; it was only at the very end that I came across these lines, which I have translated here:

'I heard that a confrontation had taken place in La Plata, so I went out and bought a newspaper. In *La Gaceta* of 25 November 1976, I was able to read the following news: *"A confrontation took place yesterday, just before 1.40 p.m., when security forces surrounded the block of houses between streets 29, 30, 55 and 56. It became clear that police attention was focused on a building on street 30, between 55 and 56. A plaque on the front of the building declared: Daniel Mariani, Bachelor of Economics. Just before the mortar attack which overcame the resistants, Major Carlos Suárez Mason of the first army corps joined the battle, as did Colonel Adolfo Siggwald, leader of the tenth infantry brigade, and Colonel Juan Ramón Camps, superintendent of the regional police force."'*

The shots came to an end around 4.55 p.m. When the police entered the house they found seven bodies, those of Roberto Cesar Porfirio, Juan Carlos Peiris, Eduardo Mendiburu Eliçabe, Diana Esmeralda Teruggi, and another three that were so charred they could not be identified.

Apart from Diana, these names were all unfamiliar to me. I would later find out that Roberto Cesar Porfirio had replaced us in the little back room: his wife had been killed by a paramilitary squad and he had had to go into hiding with his daughter. It just so happened that his daughter was out visiting her grandparents that day.

The other people killed in the attack had probably been there for a meeting. By November, the Montoneros' position had in any case greatly deteriorated: members of the group were being killed every day, or disappearing never to reappear. The 'dirty war' had entered a new phase.

The article reprinted by Gonzalo Leonidas Chaves makes no mention of Diana's baby, Clara Anahí Mariani, even though she had been in the house with her mother when the attack took place. As he did every day, her father had gone off to work in Buenos Aires, which gave him a few extra months of life: Cacho was killed by the army eight months after the attack on the rabbit house, as he walked into another La Plata house on the corner of streets 35 and 132.

A few months after reading *Los del 73*, I was lucky enough to make contact with Chicha Mariani, the mother of Daniel, or Cacho as I knew him. This meeting was the result of a string of events that still amazes me: A chance dinner with the mother of a friend, who happened to mention the name Chicha Mariani, not knowing either that I had lived in the rabbit house or how raw the whole time remained for me. An incredible coincidence. After a short correspondence with Chicha, I flew to Argentina.

*

A few years after that, in La Plata, Chicha takes me to visit what remains of the rabbit house. These days a local organization looks after it, and has turned it into a memorial site. Chicha runs this group.

You can still see where the secret printing press was located. They've even put a plaque there, explaining the reason for the strange narrow space, squeezed between two walls which are now largely in ruins. However, there is no mention of the word *embute*, not even in inverted commas.

I think the term has disappeared for ever.

The attack was clearly extremely violent.

There are no words for the feelings that overwhelmed me when I saw that place, marked for ever by death and destruction.

A mortar had made two huge holes. One in the front wall, and an identical hole in the wall between Diana and Cacho's room and the kitchen.

It had literally perforated the house.

The van is still in the garage; it's a rusty, bullet-riddled wreck.

Much of the roof has been destroyed by fire. In the back part of the house, where the printing press and the rabbits were, only fragments remain of what the place once was, nearly thirty years ago. It is nothing but ruins and rubble.

I had wanted to see the house again, and most of all I wanted to talk with Chicha and try to find out more, as much as possible.

'What about the neighbour? The blonde lady who lived next door... Is she still there?'

'The woman who lived in the house next door was terribly affected by what happened. Remember, there were heavily armed soldiers shooting from her rooftop. She started having dreadful nightmares. She couldn't live here any more. She left the area not long afterwards.'

'And Diana's baby?'

'Neighbours said that they had heard a baby crying during the attack. The baby was definitely here. Where else would she have been? The people in the house were obviously not expecting the attack, and Diana wouldn't have had time to get my granddaughter out. But her body was never found in the ruins. I am convinced that Clara Anahí survived, and was kidnapped by the army, like so many other children…'

'The attack was ferocious…'

'Yes, it was terribly violent. There are lots of theories about how Diana managed to protect her baby from the heavy artillery and firebombs used on the Montonero militants. Some think that Diana hid Clara Anahí under a mattress, in the bathtub in the little bathroom. Whatever happened, she survived. I am absolutely sure of that.'

I already know that Chicha Mariani is a remarkable person, but the more time I spend with her, the more impressed I am by her strength and courage. This woman lost her only son, as well as her daughter-in-law, under the dictatorship. And she is still looking for her disappeared granddaughter, Clara Anahí, who was probably given to a childless couple close to the regime. This happened to hundreds of other children. Some of them have now been found. Others are still searched for by their families, and Clara Anahí is one of these. She will be thirty in a few months' time.

There's one question I am still nervous to ask Cacho's mother. A question that has obsessed me for several years, and which was not answered by Chaves's book. I try clumsily to find a way to formulate it. Chicha guesses what's on my mind.

'You're wondering who betrayed them?'

Yes, that is exactly what I was wondering.

The Montonero organization had been enormously careful. And yet, the attack on the rabbit house was clearly well prepared: the extent of the military deployment, the presence of high-ranking soldiers – all this implies that the army was extremely well informed about what had been happening there, and the importance of the target. Apart from us, only Cesar knew the address of the house.

'It must have been Cesar, then?' I asked.

'Who was Cesar?'

'The leader, the one who ran the network…'

'No, it wasn't him. I don't know him by that name, but I think that the person you're talking about was killed a few days later, somewhere else in La Plata.'

Then, after a long silence:

'We too spent many years searching for the answer to this question. We don't know his exact name, but the person who told the army about the house was the man who designed the secret printing press.'

'The Engineer! But that's impossible. He always arrived hidden under a blanket, he couldn't have known where the house was. He knew only that it was somewhere in La Plata…'

'He may not have known its location, but he had no trouble identifying it. He was arrested and said he was willing to collaborate. He described the place and emphasized its strategic importance: it was the heart of the Montonero press…'

'Yes, but…'

'They flew him over the whole city in a helicopter. Methodically, neighbourhood by neighbourhood, block by block, going through the city of La Plata from above with a fine-toothed comb. That man didn't know the address, but he knew the setting off by heart, he had created the design and knew exactly how it was laid out, he even knew what materials it had been built from. He had no problem picking it out.'

'Where is he now?'

'There are many theories about that, too. Some say he's in Australia, some say South Africa. But I also met someone who told me that he too was killed by the army, not long afterwards.'

So it was the Engineer. Had he infiltrated the movement from the beginning, or simply cracked under torture? However it happened, he had known that a baby barely a few months old lived in the house.

I try to imagine him in the helicopter, flying around above the house. I imagine him saying, 'It's that house, I'm absolutely certain.'

Is it possible that he's still alive, living peacefully somewhere?

Not peacefully.

I can't believe that.

*

All of this was churning around in my mind. On my return to Paris I rushed to my old collection of Edgar Allan Poe stories and re-read 'The Purloined Letter', the one the Engineer had said was his favourite.

The action takes place in Paris. A brilliant detective, Sir Auguste Dupin, does indeed successfully apply the theory of the 'excessively obvious' that the Engineer demonstrated thirty years ago, next to the false back wall of the rabbit house.

I have a crystal-clear memory of his eyes and smile as he explained his theory. It was strange to hear the Engineer again, like this, behind the words of Dupin. But then, suddenly, the famous passage on the 'excessively obvious' made my blood run cold. I re-read it straightaway, incredulous at first.

Then horrified.

I have re-read it several times since.

I have reprinted it here:

'There is a game of puzzles,' Dupin resumed, 'which is played upon a map. One party playing requires another to find a given word – the name of town, river, state or empire – any word, in short, upon the motley and perplexed surface of the chart. A novice in the game generally seeks to embarrass his opponents by giving them the most minutely lettered names; but the adept selects such words as stretch, in large characters, from one end of the chart to the other. These, like the over-largely lettered signs and placards of the street, escape observation by dint of being excessively obvious.'

Ever since re-reading this passage, and hearing the Engineer's voice ringing out over Dupin's words, I can't help seeing the Montonero militants, who thought they were protecting themselves by insisting that the Engineer hide under a blanket whenever he came to the house, as the 'novices' in a game not dissimilar to that described by Poe's character. As an 'adept' and a sharp reader, the Engineer had just transposed the game that Dupin described on a 'map', onto the layout of a real city. He had simply changed the scale. And the stakes.

In this way, he had not the slightest need to know the number on the door, or even of the street, because he was able to read, from above, the lines and features that gave away the house. He knew how to make out the large characters. The over-largely lettered signs.

*

But no one could turn an Edgar Allan Poe story into a weapon to serve the dirty war. No one could use such subtlety and intelligence to massacre people. And if someone did do that, well, he had no right.

I know there are subtle machinations; too subtle. Sometimes they are barbaric. Strategies to dominate other people, and to have the last word. But can it ever be worth